Step it up!

Fun pieces for piano grades 2–3 (US: Early Int.–Int.)

LOUISE CHAMBERLAIN

CONTENTS

© 2003 by Faber Music Ltd and Alfred Publishing Co., Inc.
First published in 2003 jointly by Faber Music Ltd and Alfred Publishing Co., Inc.
Bloomsbury House 74–77 Great Russell Street London WC1B 3DA
Cover design by Shireen Nathoo Design
Music processed by MusicSet 2000
Printed in England by Caligraving Ltd
All rights reserved

ISBN10: 0-571-52181-9
EAN13: 978-0-571-52181-4

Distributed in the Americas and Australasia by Alfred Publishing Co., Inc.
Distributed throughout the rest of the world by Faber Music Ltd

FABER *ff* MUSIC

Smart cookie

Louise Chamberlain

Make believe

The Entertainer

Scott Joplin
arr. L.C.

Space station 2

Caprice

Nicolò Paganini
arr. L.C.

The secret garden

In the hall of the mountain king

Edvard Grieg
arr. L.C.

Sapphire blues

Gentle waltz time ♩ = 96

Hurricane Harry

Stormy ♩. = 112–116

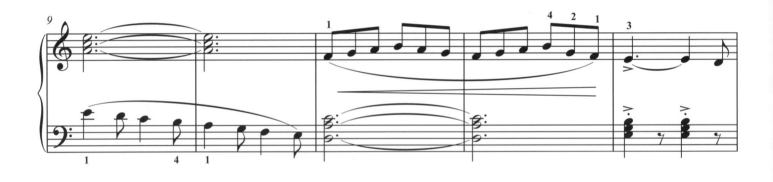

Blues for a pink cadillac

Jig along

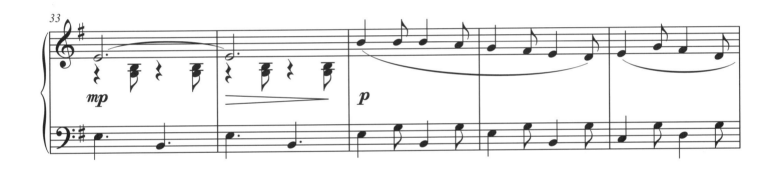

Time travelling

King of the swing

King of the swing

Step it up 2

Step it up 2

STEP IT UP!

Move your playing onwards and upwards with *Step it up!*

Packed full of original jazzy pieces by Louise Chamberlain – with imaginative arrangements of well-known tunes, and duets too – these carefully graded volumes are guaranteed to liven up your practice no end.

Grades 0–1 Ranging from the jolly 'Sunny-side up' to the laid-back

STEP IT UP!
Fun pieces
for piano
Grades 0–1
ISBN 0-571-52180-0
Grades 2–3
ISBN 0-571-52181-9

'Huckleberry', via rusty robots and bears with sore heads, this simple yet imaginative collection is ideal for the very beginner pianist.

Grades 2–3 In this, the next stage up for pianists, Louise Chamberlain offers more varied pieces in her characteristically groovy style. With 'Blues for a pink cadillac', 'Space station 2' and 'King of the swing', the fun continues …

So whether practising at home or performing to your friends, take your playing to another level with *Step it up!* – and prepare to step up a grade at the same time!